PROMISES WORTH KEEPING

THE SONGS OF FRED SMALL
VOLUME 2

Maureen + Donald,
Keep on singing!!

5/17/13

◯ YELLOW MOON PRESS ◯
CAMBRIDGE, MASSACHUSETTS

ISBN: 0-938756-45-1

Cover Photos: Susan Wilson

Production & Design: Robert B. Smyth

Editorial & Production assistance: Robin McFarlane & Joel Husenits

Music Transcription: Benjamin Groff

Music Notation: Kim & Steve Araiza - Scooter Typesetting

Yellow Moon Press
P.O. Box 1316
Cambridge, MA 02238
(617) 776 - 2230
(617) 776 - 8246 - Fax

If the world were merely seductive,
that would be easy. If it were merely challenging,
that would be no problem.

But I arise in the morning torn between
a desire to improve the world,
And a desire to enjoy the world.

This makes it hard to plan the day.

E. B. White

Contents

In the fall of 1979, a group of Clams who were planning the occupation of the Seabrook nuke began gathering after evenings of canvassing for Mass. Fair Share and 9-to-5 at the Idler in Cambridge. In a smoky back room of this little basement bar on Mt. Auburn Street, Manager Lenny Rothenberg greeted all the rads (and aspiring rads) by name, and the revolution was plotted to tunes by the likes of Robin Flower, Si Kahn, Patty Lakin, and Fred Small. We used to scramble for a table right up front, practically in the lap of whoever was on stage, which made for a pretty intimate evening with the performer. This is where I (and lots of other lesbians) fell in love with Fred.

In those days, Fred was just phasing out of lawyering to become a full-time musician. He had a heavy mustache and beard and very serious, studious glasses. Looking back now, I think he may have been a little shy and even a little nervous, but we didn't give him a chance to remember that. We learned every word of every song, by heart, and we sang really loud...we were obnoxious, but enthusiastic. From our bedrooms to our jobs, from the streets to the jails, Fred's music was the accompaniment to our lives.

After the Idler closed, riding the wave of his huge local following, Fred went upscale and booked at Passim. By now, I was experiencing Poverty at divinity school, and I clearly remember weighing the price of a concert ticket against a haircut. I let my hair grow. Fred's clarity and lucidity about current events, his articulate championship of the earth and his infectious passion for all the dispossessed, his dry wit and disarming good humor...to hear Fred sing his songs meant more education and a lot more joy in one evening than any of us got in a week. It still does.

I moved and moved and moved again, but Fred never lost touch, and he never lost his touch. His fans stretch around the world now, across the United States and Canada, around to Australia, Japan, and England, and back again, to Cambridge. And his commitment to his fans is tremendous. When Marnie and I brought our daughters home from South America, there was even a lullaby waiting for them. Fred calls it "Everything Possible." He believes that, and he inspires all of us to believe it, too.

These days, Fred is clean-shaven (no more glasses), with the body of a god, and two earrings in his left ear. Deeply intent on "walking the walk," Fred's traded in his car for a T pass and a bicycle, and keeps a fine, simple home filled with good food and wonderful friends. As always, he speaks and sings his ringing truth with an eloquence informed by an open heart. Above all, he loves deeply, and he is deeply loved. Open up this book and sing these songs...I want you to meet my friend, Fred Small. I know you will love him, too.

Kim Crawford Harvie
Arlington Street Church, Boston

PREFACE

I wish I could see the world every day through a child's eyes—every color bright and vivid, every sound resonant and arresting, every experience an adventure, every person a potential new friend.

When I listen to folk music at a small coffeehouse, I sometimes recapture that feeling of wonder, delight, and deep appreciation I first felt as a child for a singer, a guitar, and a rapt audience singing along.

In those days everyone sang, it seemed, and nearly everybody was picking up a guitar and playing it, not worrying about whether they sounded as good as what they heard on their 33-r.p.m. record albums from Capitol or Vanguard or Elektra, just intoxicated with the 100-proof joy of making music.

The song was greater than the singer, interpretation finer than mimicry. Songs traveled far and fast with no radio airplay whatsoever, transmitted from festival to open mike to hootenanny and back again the other way as if by talking drum. Magazines like *Sing Out!* and *Broadside* brought still more songs to the mailbox, awaited as eagerly as if they had been premiums earned through the excruciating accumulation of cereal box tops.

Songbooks were another treasure, a mother lode of folk ore to be mined for hours and days and weeks. *The Fireside Book of Folk Songs, The Weavers' Song Book, The Tom Paxton Songbook, Songs of Phil Ochs, The Judy Collins Songbook*—all brought into my life new places, people, stories, melodies, and ways of thinking about the world. I would hunch over them with my guitar, awkwardly working out the chords, feeling I had somehow found my tiny place in an ancient lineage of common men and women who ennobled themselves and their communities through song.

So when Yellow Moon Press in 1986 offered to publish a book of my songs, I felt honored beyond words to join the tradition of folksingers whose songs are compiled in books. Perhaps some novice guitar player would one day sit hunched over my book, and the cycle would be complete.

Now it's eight years later, I have three more albums to add to the first three, and lots of people have been asking for a new songbook with the new songs.

I've changed in eight years. I hope you have, too!

(My friend Charlie King tells a wonderful tuning joke. He says, "You know, guitar strings are a lot like people. They keep changing. And that can be frustrating. But when they stop changing, they're dead.")

I'm more at peace with myself, more content with my life, more attuned to the present moment than to the past or the future. I'm not signed to a major label. I don't play to huge concert halls. I've never won a Grammy. But my songs help people cry, and laugh, and think about things in new ways. Babies go to sleep to "Everything Possible." Teenagers memorize "Annie" and "Denmark 1943." Adults bring "Light in the Hall" and "I Will Stand Fast" to their therapy sessions. I make a difference in people's lives. There is no reward greater.

The lesson of my youth was that if you wanted something, you had to make it happen. Go for it. "Just do it."

The lesson of my adulthood is to let things happen. Often they turn out better than what was so urgently sought after.

When I began my music career a dozen years ago, I was scared of failure; so I pushed hard for success. To anyone to whom I was thoughtless, self-centered or rude, I apologize. Arrogance is only the mask of fear.

The practice of meditation has helped me see the world more clearly. I mean that literally. My sight seems keener, sensations more intense, people more interesting. Each day brings new miracles. (For those interested in meditation, I recommend *The Miracle of Mindfulness*, *Being Peace*, and *Peace Is Every Step*, all books by Thich Nhat Hanh. Bob Fellows also offers a fine introduction to meditation on his cassette, *Awareness and Meditation*, available from Mind Matters, Inc., P.O. Box 16557, Minneapolis, MN 55416.)

For me, the calm of meditation would have been inaccessible without the opportunity to tell my story to a caring listener. Many of us were raised not to acknowledge our pain or the pain of those around us. (Lou and Peter Berryman sing a devastatingly funny song called "We Don't Talk about That," which pretty much says it all.)

I don't think real healing is possible without first acknowledging how much we hurt and feeling the grief and anger we have buried inside. Whether through therapy, peer counseling, or simply the tender listening of a friend, we need the chance to release our pain, and heal our wounds.

But we don't need to become mired in our pain. As Thich Nhat Hanh writes in Being Peace, "Life is filled with suffering, but it is also filled with many wonders, like the blue sky, the sunshine, the eyes of a baby. To suffer is not enough. We must also be in touch with the wonders of life. They are within us and all around us, everywhere, any time."

Over the years my songs, I think, have grown more personal and less facile, less glib. I am less afraid to reveal myself in my writing and performance. I search harder for the fresh, unexpected image, though I remain simple and straightforward in my writing. ("Quirky" is one label that has never stuck to me!) I venture more often beyond the story-song form to convey a feeling or message.

But, as ever, my songs are about the things I care most about: community, cooperation, compassion, courage, fairness, simplicity, the earth, peace, and yes, love.

It has become fashionable, especially in the media, to dismiss such concerns with the derisive epithet "politically correct"—one of the most grossly abused phrases of the last decade. I'm sure some leftists once upon a time used it seriously. Fortunately, *I* never heard them! Instead, I heard it used in a gently self-satirical way by activists who knew that the idea of a single, inarguable "party line" is dangerous, undemocratic, and self-defeating.

In the late eighties, reactionary pundits discovered the phrase and used it as a club to attack efforts by educational institutions to diversify curricula and protect students from insulting and demeaning language. The tension between the right to free speech, on the one hand, and the right to respect and safety in one's academic or residential community, on the other, is a legitimate subject of debate. But the idea that our colleges and universities have surrendered to left-wing orthodoxy is a bad joke.

These days reporters and commentators trot out the phrase whenever anyone tries to do anything to oppose racism, sexism, homophobia, discrimination against people with disabilities, ageism, poverty, pollution, disease, war—in short, whenever anyone tries to make the world a better place. Idealism, sneer the critics, is just "politically correct."

Idealism, in fact, is how we live, how we survive. By helping each other. By caring for more than our own profit. By loving each other.

Otherwise, what's the point?

The songs in this book are a few markers I've left along my path. Perhaps they will be helpful to you on your journey as well. But your journey is your own.

A song is only a signpost indicating a direction. Maybe not even the right direction at the time. Maybe the right direction some other time. Maybe not.

If you sing a song of mine, I will be honored.

If you sing your own song, I will be more honored still.

Fred Small
Cambridge, Massachusetts
Autumn, 1994

THE HILLS OF AYALON

"Understanding and love," says Thich Nhat Hanh, the Vietnamese Buddhist teacher, "are not two things, but just one." Demonization of enemies as something alien, less than human, is a precondition of war. Otherwise, how could entire populations be moved to kill—personally or through surrogates called soldiers—other human beings?

There is in Israel a settlement called, in Hebrew, Neve Shalom, and in Arabic, Wahat Al-Salam, where Jews and Arabs live and work together and lead workshops where Jewish and Arab young people can learn more about each other. This song is based on an actual dialogue at one of these workshops. My thanks to Martha Kransdorf and Judy Wisch for bringing the story to my attention.

Copyright 1988 Pine Barrens Music (BMI)

In the hills of Ay-a-lon___ a-bove the bro-ken earth

Two boys shout and play with a ball___ on a

field of shrub and dirt Di-vid-ed sons of A-bra-ham

ex-haust-ed em-brace___ Prince of Is-lam

pride of Ju-dah know each___ oth-er's___ face

Chorus

"If we met on the sands of Si-nai un-der a mol-ten

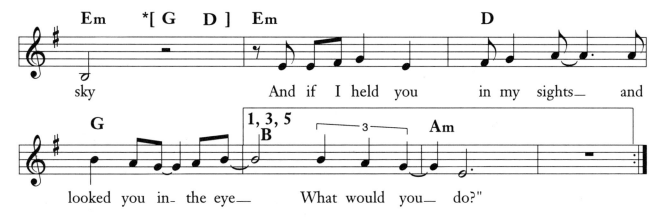

2nd and 3rd chorus only

In the hills of Ayalon above the broken earth
Two boys shout and play with a ball on a field of shrub and
  dirt
Divided sons of Abraham exhausted embrace
Prince of Islam pride of Judah know each other's face

"If we met on the sands of Sinai under a molten sky
And if you held me in your sights and looked me in the eye
What would you do?"
"If we met on the sands of Sinai under a molten sky
And if I held you in my sights and looked you in the eye
I would shoot you dead"

In the hills of Ayalon that once were no man's land
Shepherds chase their wandering sheep and lead them home
  again
"My grandfather died at Dachau—never will I forget"
"The British set fire to my grandfather's village and left
  twelve Moslem dead"

"If we met on the cliffs of Haramoun stunned by the rocket's
  flash
And if you found my heart exposed and a pistol in your grasp
What would you do?"
"If we met on the cliffs of Haramoun stunned by the rocket's
  flash
And if I found your heart exposed and a pistol in my grasp
I would take you prisoner hide you away then set you free"

In the hills of Ayalon the young ones play a game
Toss an orange in the air and call each other's name
Ricky Shimon Shalom Naomi—catch it before it falls
Youssef Hassan Amal Amira tear down the walls

"If we met by the river Jordan under a rain of nails
And if you raised your rifle up and your aim could not fail
What would you do?"
"If we met by the river Jordan under a rain of nails
And if I raised my rifle up and my aim could not fail
I would put down my gun open my arms and weep"

DIAMONDS OF ANGER

One of President Ronald Reagan's more breathtakingly ignorant remarks was that apartheid had been eliminated in South Africa—this while apartheid was in full force, and Nelson Mandela languished in prison! It occurred to me that if the president of the United States (however spaced-out) could be so ill informed, then perhaps many more Americans had only a nebulous idea of the real-life horrors of apartheid.

Bigotry and oppression are all too common around the globe, but their codification in law is especially heinous, putting the weight and sanction of the state on the side of hatred.

Copyright 1988 Pine Barrens Music (BMI)

Eyes— a-mazed— and smil-ing through doors— and

bro-ken win-dows strain-ing———— to touch

The boy rolls the hoop past the barricade
Pushing it fast with a stick that he made from a coathanger
The hoop is a wheel of rusted steel from a junkyard bicycle
The girl on the corner plays the guitar
It's a petrol can with strings of wire
She sings a song from the tribal days
But the words are new—she sings amandla

Blond surfers on white sandy beaches
Wait for the perfect wave
The sky has no clouds at sunset they go home
The signs say no dogs or natives allowed
Nervous white boys in combat gear
Speed through the township in armored trucks
People scatter but the soldiers run them down
Kick them until blood runs from their mouths

CHORUS:
Crossroads
We are diamonds of anger we are brilliant gold
Every blow makes us stronger the chain cannot hold
We are rocks against tear gas we are songs against guns
We are life against terror we have already won

The old woman waits for the broken down bus
To take her from this shantytown of tin and paper
No toilet no running water
The street is already hot
She rides to the white homes of Johannesburg
To mop the kitchen tile polish the silver
Wipe the babies' bottoms she must leave by nightfall

Sixteen on trial for plotting revolution
Charged with singing songs of freedom
Or being present when these songs were sung
Or writing pamphlets or speaking at meetings
Botha tells the whites what they want to hear
The only votes he needs are theirs
Crazed with their backs to the sea
Drunk with the fear of retribution

CHORUS

BRIDGE:
Black babies white babies still reach for each other
Fingers stretching from the passing prams
Eyes amazed and smiling through doors and broken
    windows
Straining to touch

Behind the silence of Pollsmoor Prison
Nelson Mandela reads the international press
Receives foreign visitors
The chief in exile the lion at bay
Give up violence say the key-jangling jackels
He answers let those who shoot my people
Beat with whips torture with electrodes
Let these renounce violence and I will walk free

Teenagers born since he was imprisoned
Hear his voice though they have never seen him
Feel the tremor of righteous fury
A vision burning a tidal wave coming
New leaders born in the schoolyards and churches
Forged in the mines singing at funerals
Turning to block the blow as it's falling
Seizing the whiphand standing rejoicing

CHORUS

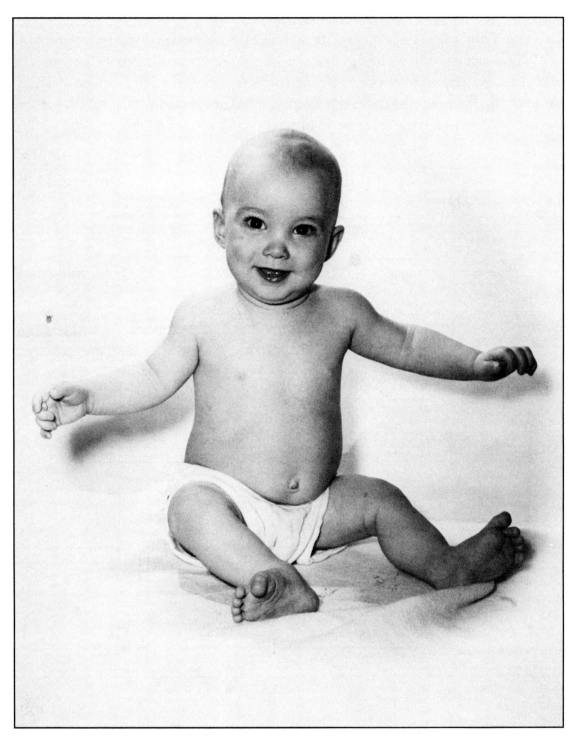

Small Fred

I Will Stand Fast

All of us get hurt. It helps if there is someone who will listen gently to our story, hearing us out without judgment or criticism, giving us room to feel our feelings without interjecting their own. I am grateful to know that this song has been widely used to assist the healing of survivors of child abuse. But whatever our history, it has not always been easy. We all need someone who will stand fast for us, as we in turn will stand fast for them.

You are safe in the day light— at last

Night-mare and fear they have no pow-er

here I will stand fast

Coda

I will stand fast

The echoes of childhood whisper violence
Cold wind beating out of the past
Rage in your throat muffled silence
Hold on I will stand fast

In the darkness your guardians had left you
Cold wind beating out of the past
None to hear your cries none to defend you
Hold on I will stand fast

CHORUS:
I will stand fast I will stand fast
You are safe in the daylight at last
Nightmare and fear they have no power here
I will stand fast

I will listen to the terrors that tried you
Cold wind beating out of the past
I will cradle the child that breathes inside you
Hold on I will stand fast

Though you take the shape of a hundred ancient horrors
Cold wind beating out of the past
Though you strike at me and flee into your sorrow
Hold on I will stand fast

CHORUS

Birds flash upon a branch in winter
Cold wind beating out of the past
Ice in the sun begins to splinter
Hold on I will stand fast

You will walk with no fetters to bind you
Cold wind beating out of the past
All the love you have wanted will find you
Hold on I will stand fast

CHORUS

AT THE ELBE

Governments so often try to divide us with jingoism and whip us into martial mania, but our common humanity keeps rearing its beautiful head.

This song is sung from the vantage point, more or less, of Joe Polowski, whose story I first encountered in Studs Terkel's magnificent oral history of World War II *"The Good War"*. (Please note that Terkel himself put the title in quotes. "Good" is a relative term.) Although Joe died before I began my research, I talked with his widow, son, and several of his fellow veterans who, like Joe, had met the enemy and discovered a friend. The whole story is told in *Yanks Meet Reds*, edited by Mark Scott and Semyon Krasilshchik (Capra Press, 1988).

Chorus

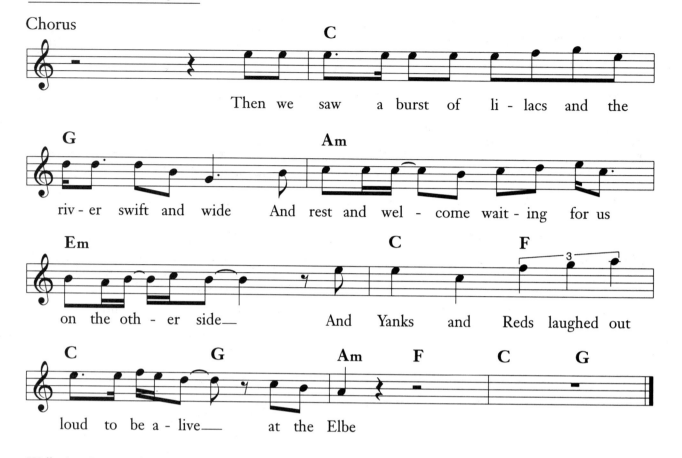

C

Then we saw a burst of li - lacs and the

G   Am

riv - er swift and wide   And rest and wel - come wait - ing for us

Em   C   F

on the oth - er side___   And Yanks and Reds laughed out

C   G   Am   F   C   G

loud to be a - live___   at the Elbe

Well mister I just overheard you talking through your drink
How the Russians lie like rugs how they've pushed us to the brink
Now sit right here beside me I've an old man's tale to tell
How Yanks and Reds were friends once at the Elbe

My name is Joe Polowski I hitched up in '41
Left my sweetheart in Chicago and I learned to fire a gun
The fog in the Ardennes so thick you could not see your nose
Nor the ghosts in the Belgian wood advancing through the snow

We left our dead behind us and we scaled the Dragon's Teeth
With screaming mimis overhead not one of us could sleep
Some fell to the enemy some fell to the creeping cold
And I killed a German sniper who was not fourteen years old

BRIDGE:
When a soldier takes a hit my friend it ain't like Hollywood
Bone and guts go flying and everywhere there's blood
For a moment he is mystified there must be some mistake
As it all drains out in a crimson lake

Then April turned the weather and likewise the tide of war
As haggard hungry Germans surrendered by the score
And thank god for the Russians who took the battle's brunt
And broke the back of the Wermacht along the eastern front
Then

CHORUS:
We saw a burst of lilacs and the river swift and wide
And rest and welcome waiting for us on the other side
And Yanks and Reds laughed out loud to be alive at the Elbe

We caught the glint of water and upon the distant shore
Men and trucks and horses not German and not ours
No bridge to cross but at the dock a boat securely tied
We blew the chain and rowed like demons for the other side

But when we stepped up on the land oh Jesus what a sight
Blackened bodies of civilians like driftwood piled high
Cut down by stray artillery—what the hell is it all for
We knelt and cursed the cruelty and madness men call war

BRIDGE:
Three Russians approached us we shook hands and then embraced
Stalingrad had traced its lines of sadness on their face
Upon that field of corpses these weary happy men
Swore an oath that it must never happen again
And then we wept and cheered and spoke in languages unknown
They poured us Russian vodka by god we drank it down
We sang "The Volga Boatman" they sang "Tavern in the Town"
I never kissed so many men as on that afternoon when

CHORUS

But no sooner were we stateside than the cold war headlines
  read
Commies in the unions commies under every bed
Hurrah the Nazi devil's down long live the devil Red
And not one word about the oath we swore amongst the
  dead

There are kids today who'll tell you we fought Russia in the
  war
There are armchair heroes set to settle some old score
There are profiteers and pushers primed to send young men
  once more
To blow themselves to glory on some godforsaken shore

BRIDGE:
So drape my coffin with the flag of the good old USA
Let Yanks in army khaki and Reds in Russian gray
Lower me so gently into the German clay
And speak again the oath we swore that day

When

CHORUS

IF I WERE A MOOSE

Back in the mid-1980s, a moose wandered out of the Vermont woods and got a sort of a crush on a dairy cow named Jessica, immediately drawing the attention of a rapt nation and the not entirely wrapped media. When I heard the story, I was inspired. I thought, "My god! It takes a lot of courage to date outside your species!"

In an increasingly diverse society and a shrinking world, we can all learn something from the moose and the cow.

Copyright 1988 Pine Barrens Music (BMI)

Would you lead me down the re - ceiv-ing line— And bold - ly boast— "This

moose is mine!" Would your par - ents watch us graze—

Shake their heads "It's just a phase"— Or would they thank the stars—

— a - bove— Their pre - cious heif - er's found her love?—

Bridge

But if you think this thing— will last— Could he learn to moo— and

eat our grass— Shed his ant-lers in the dirt—

Could you per-suade him to con - vert?

Coda

Might you per - mit a good-night kiss Could you learn to love—

wet moose lips? If I_____ were a moose—
and you were a cow—— If you were a cow—
— and I were a moose

If I were a moose and you were a cow
Would you love me anyhow?
Would you introduce me to your folks
Would you tell your friends "No moose jokes!"
If I were a moose and you were a cow

Would you invite me to your club
And risk a cruel bovine snub
Would you lead me down the receiving line
And boldly boast "This moose is mine!"

Would your parents watch us graze
Shake their heads "It's just a phase"
Or would they thank the stars above
Their precious heifer's found her love?

Would your grandparents change their will?
They'd really expected a Holstein bull
"For this we toiled before the plow—
You bring home someone who's not even a cow

There's lots of proper stock around
Like that nice young Guernsey at Farmer Brown's
Or that last one we ridiculed and cursed
On second thought you could do worse

Bridge:
But if you think this thing will last
Could he learn to moo and eat our grass
Shed his antlers in the dirt
Could you persuade him to convert?"

If our anatomies did not quite fit
Would you make the best of it
Would you nuzzle up so near
And hum sweet cow tunes in my ear?

Or would you sadly break it off
When all the hillside sneered and scoffed
"You know those moose are all the same
They're lazy they're stupid they come from Maine"

It's true things slip a moose's mind
That cows remember all the time
Bulbous nose and knobby knees
A coat that harbors ticks and fleas

But a moose can be a handy thing
When hungry wolves come visiting
In icy gust of winter storm
Our fur is deep and dry and warm

And someday should your milk run dry
And farmer stare with baleful eye
In dead of night I'd slip your noose
And lead you home to the land of moose
If I were a moose and you were a cow

Bridge:
If hunters came to do me harm
Would you hide me in the barn
Would all the herd come on the run
And glare until they dropped their guns?

Might you permit a good-night kiss
Could you learn to love wet moose lips?
If I were a moose and you were a cow
If you were a cow and I were a moose

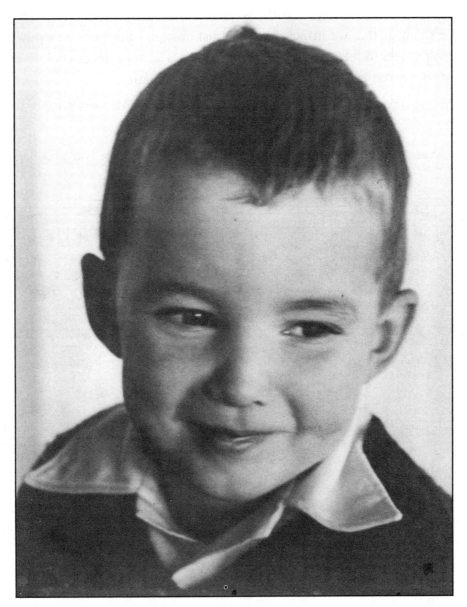

Fred's winning smile in 1955

EVERY MAN

Not every man plays the role, but every man is taught. Every man is threatened, and too many men are brutalized into being what the world cynically calls "men." Men must take responsibility for the hurt that we inflict, and we must change. But guilt and powerlessness are not the answer. We need to feel, to know ourselves, and, at a very deep level, to respect ourselves. We need to awaken from a long slumber, a kind of death.

I believe that no one hurts another before being first hurt. Abusers are not born, but made. There are no demons. The cycle of violence must end.

Capo on 2nd Fret

♩ = 174

Copyright 1988 Pine Barrens Music (BMI)

Am

I was born in the cit-y— hos - pi-tal

G   Am

Torn from dark - ness in-to the light—

First man I— saw— was the first to hit me

G   F   G   Am

First wom-an I saw said "hush don't— cry"

Chorus

Am   C

Ev' - ry man gon-na be a sol - dier

G   Am

Ev' - ry man— be cut to kill—

G

Ev'- ry man— look-ing o-ver his shoul - der

D **F** **G** **Am**

Ev'- ry man be shak-ing— still

Bridge **E** **Am**

I have killed but I am not a kil - ler—

E **E7** **Am**

I have cried out at the dev - il in the dark

A7 **F** **C**

I have reached out through the bars— of my con - fine - ment

Dm **E**

I have watched the tow- er I built fall a - part

E7

I was born in the city hospital
Torn from darkness into the light
First man I saw was the first to hit me
First woman I saw said hush don't cry

I played with girls till I was six years old
Guys told me you don't want no girl a friend
You can kiss 'em you can touch 'em
When you screw 'em you'll be a man

CHORUS:
Every man gonna be a soldier
Every man be cut to kill
Every man looking over his shoulder
Every man be shaking still

I played war king of the mountain
When I hurt I did not cry kids'd laugh
Big guy hit me hot fire in the stomach
I hit a little guy put him on his back

Mike and me eight-year-old cowboys
He said c'mon whatsa matter you a queer
We went to Molly's pulled her down and kissed her
She got up walked inside without a word

CHORUS

Came the war to my generation
Government said son it's your time make us proud
Some went to jail some went to Canada
Some went over some went crazy some went down

I walk the streets jagged with strangers
Wait for the gauntlet to be hurled
Push to shove edge of a razor
Make something of it he'll cut you good

CHORUS

BRIDGE:
I have killed but I am not a killer
I have cried out at the devil in the dark
I have reached out through the bars of my confinement
I have watched the tower I built fall apart

Gonna listen for the breathing of the baby
Gonna hold him in my arms when he cries
Gonna meet my lover's gaze without turning
Gonna see myself and be satisfied

FINAL CHORUS:
Every man got love abiding
Every man got a hurt unhealed
Every man got a heart in hiding
Every man gonna be revealed

To be consistent in achieving inner peace,
we must perceive a world in which everyone is innocent.

Gerald Jampolsky

Fred in 1958 enjoying an apple

SCOTT AND JAMIE

This song tells the true story of Don Babets and David Jean, a gay couple into whose caring, capable hands were placed two abused foster children. After the media got hold of the story, Governor Michael Dukakis ordered the boys summarily removed. Perhaps the governor was simply ignorant and homophobic. More likely, he was covering his right flank in anticipation of his presidential bid. Either way, it was a grievous injustice to the foster parents, to the gay community, and especially to the children.

— nor   he gave   the   or - der

So - cial work - er phoned— "Have them read-y at three"

Call us America's sweethearts—We found a place in Roxbury
Where we can meet the mortgage go to church on Sunday
I teach communion class and David leads the choir
Ten years together thinking about children

Lots of children out there beat up beat down hoping
For a home and a harbor a hand that doesn't hit
Where the form said "father" and "mother" we had to cross it out
"Father" and "father" that's David and me

Twelve months of waiting suddenly two little boys on our doorstep
Scared and crying gave them a bath and tucked them in
Three-year-old Jamie little brother Scott
Jamie had a bruise like a boot in the middle of his back

CHORUS:
Love is love no matter who no matter where
Love is love and a child knows when it's there
They can pry away the fingers that graced these walls with dirt
They can pull us apart they can lie oh they can hurt
But love leaves a trace and the heart holds a place for love's return

McDonald's and K-Mart—do you know how hard it is to find kid's shoes?
Scott's first haircut grinning and a little confused
Outside the aquarium baseball jackets red and blue
A picture is like time that's standing still

Jamie was a scrapper he punched his brother decked the kid next door
He threw a plate at David then ducked and cowered waiting for the blow

After supper I held him close "You're safe here this is your home"
And the rains came to the parched and broken earth

BRIDGE:
But the papers smelled the headlines—gay parents two little innocent boys
TV news on the front porch politicians made a lot of noise
Liberal governor he gave the order
Social worker phoned "Have them ready at three"

Picked Jamie up at daycare kids were running shouting as they played
We didn't want to tell him maybe the governor could have explained
Jamie was screaming when we strapped him in the welfare car
David said "We love you" and they were gone

BRIDGE:
You find out who your friends are some came round some just let it go
Rallies on the common people singing people saying no
This is crazy—but Scott and Jamie
Are still pinballs in a busted machine

The kitchen's clean and quiet we changed the furniture around
Still keep Scott's rabbit—in the middle of the night sometimes I wake to the sound
Of a little one crying when there's nothing there at all
David holds me says "Go back to sleep"

CHORUS

Fred's graduation picture from The Taft School, 1970

DENMARK 1943

All the stories in this song are true, and there are many more, equally moving, that I couldn't fit in a song. I love these stories because they tell of people reaching beyond their borders, their community, their identity, to give someone else a hand, even at great danger to themselves.

After writing this song, I learned from Rabbi Melchior's son that the story of his father slugging the skipper, which I had read in historical accounts, is an exaggeration. His father, he says, would never have struck anyone in anger, "but he could knock you down with his words." So I like to think the song is still metaphorically true.

And it's Eich-man and Himm-ler are turn-ing the screws— The Fuhrer they say grows im - pa-tient "How can it be Den-mark's Jews still walk free Af-ter three years of kind oc-cu - pa-tion? We will take them like sheep in their beds as they sleep On the sec-ond night of their new year De-vout-ly at home they'll be help-less a-lone— When they cry out no one will—— hear"

But Duck-witz the Ger-man tells Hed-toft the Dane "My
friend I have dan-ger-ous news— In three hours— the trans-port ships
will set at an-chor— You must warn them warn all the Jews" Soon
good Rab-bi Mel-chi – or stands in the sy – na-gogue
"There'll be no ser-vice to-day— The raids come to-mor-row dwell
not on your sor-row By night-fall we must be a-way" And it's

Chorus
fi – re up the die-sel and look out for swells— We're
leav-ing Es-per-gaer-de be-hind us Who strike at our friends strike

us as well We'll pray the pa-trol boats don't find___ us When the

si-rens are wail-ing and shouts fill_ the night Nev-er will you stand a-

lone So it's o - ver the Ore - sund Till the

day we can wel-come you home

Bridge

Fro - zen with fright in the Oc - to - ber night___ Fami-lies_

_ hud-dle in base-ments and barns Mis-tak-ing each breath for the

an - gel of death_ The Ges - ta-po the shot the a-larm Then down

in - to the hold_with the stench and the cold and drug all the ba-bies with

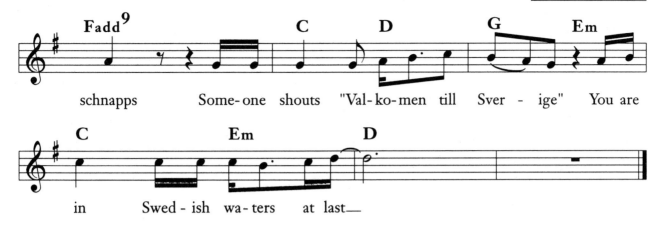

schnapps   Some-one shouts "Val-ko-men till Sver - ige"   You are

in   Swed - ish wa - ters   at last—

And it's Eichmann and Himmler are turning the screws
The Fuhrer they say grows impatient "How can it be
    Denmark's Jews still walk free
After three years of kind occupation?
We will take them like sheep in their beds as they sleep
On the second night of their new year
Devoutly at home they'll be helpless alone
When they cry out no one will hear"

But Duckwitz the German tells Hedtoft the Dane
"My friend I have dangerous news
In three hours the transport ships will set at anchor
 You must warn them warn all the Jews"
Soon good Rabbi Melchior stands in the synagogue
"There'll be no service today
The raids come tomorrow dwell not on your sorrow
By nightfall we must be away"

CHORUS:
And it's fire up the diesel and look out for swells
We're leaving Espergaerde behind us
Who strike at our friends strike us as well
We'll pray the patrol boats don't find us
When the sirens are wailing and shouts fill the night
Never will you stand alone
So it's over the Oresund
Till the day we can welcome you home

Sompolinski the tailor on the eve of Rosh Hashana
Gathers his family near
"The Lord is my light and salvation
Whom on this earth shall I fear?"
When a young Danish gentile steps into the glow
Of the candle with tears flowing down
"Good neighbors flee—I pray you believe me"
And as quickly the young man is gone

Christian policemen shopkeepers and teachers
Tell their friends of the quickening storm
While students on bicycles race through the streets
Searching for Jews to be warned
And Katlev the foreman blurts out to the trainman
"My family has no place to hide"
"Well bring 'em to my house" the stranger replies
"And we'll spit in the damn Nazis' eyes"

CHORUS

Ellen Nielsen the fishwife in the port of Dragor
Has no use for political views
She'll call out the catch "Fresh salmon! Fresh cod!"
Comes a whisper "Please help we are Jews"
"But if you are Jews you're not safe on the street
 I know a man with a sail"
Till moonrise they sleep in the shade of her eaves
And escape on the fisherman's keel

Rabbi Melchior hires a young trawlerman
To ferry his family across
After twelve hours afloat in a scurfy old boat
Morning light shows the same Danish coast
Says the skipper "I'm afraid of the German blockade
So we've motored in circles around"
The rabbi gives a shout with one blow knocks him out
And steers a straight line 'cross the sound

BRIDGE:
Frozen with fright in the October night
Families huddle in basements and barns
Mistaking each breath for the angel of death
The Gestapo the shot the alarm
Then down into the hold with the stench and the cold
And drug all the babies with schnapps
Someone shouts "Valkommen till Sverige
You are in Swedish waters at last"

Seven thousands of Jews smuggled over to Sweden
By fishermen nurses and priests
Hitler sends Eichmann to hunt them down
But his quarry have vanished like mist
When the war's over the Jews return
Cheers and flowers adorn their way home
"We're not heroes or martyrs" so say the Danes
"We were just looking after our own"

CHORUS

. . . And today we will welcome you home
And today we welcome you home

THIS LOVE

How we treat those closest to us has everything to do with how governments treat the peoples of the earth. Love creates ripples as on a pond, emanating ever outward. A smile can trigger a chain reaction of happiness. We need to cultivate peace in our daily lives as we work for it around the world.

Sometimes people ask what is it like
This love that's holding me unfolding me
Sometimes people ask what's the difference
That we see in your days
It's not romance if romance is a dream world
It's not bliss if bliss is ignorance
And if I tried to tell the truth of us
The closest I'd come could be this

If for just one moment
People all over the world could know this love
Armies would hold their fire
Soldiers would unlace their boots
And play soccer on the shrouded fields
Let the tanks rust where they stand
Take hold of a foreign hand
"Tell me of life in your native land"

If for just one moment
People all over the world could know this love
Ancient tribes betrayed
Sometimes slaver sometimes slave
Would lay wreathes upon the graves
And gather under a spreading tree
Saying "Hear our tragedy
And we will listen to you"

And the bully who beats on the weaker one
Would say "My God what have I done?
Has it come to this?"
And the victim who bore it so long
Would be strong enough to stop it
And find a way to forgive

If for just one moment
People all over the world could know this love
People on line at the bank
Would whistle and yodel and dance
The teller would say "Just fill in the blanks
For whatever you need today"

People around the block
Would leave the front door unlocked
And all you gotta do is knock to be welcomed
When you get this close to someone
There is no blaming no mistaking
You know what they've been through
And the courage it's constantly taking

If for just one moment
People all over the world could know this love
If for just one moment
People all over the world
Could know this love

Fred's Yale graduation photo, 1974

JAGUAR

The rain forest is not far away in foreign lands. It is in the food we eat, the clothing we wear, the TV commercials we thoughtlessly take in, pretending they don't affect us. Barry Commoner's First Law of Ecology: Everything is connected to everything else. (Buddhism meets biology!)

Mon-keys are screech-ing in flight The spires of the Ara - wak cut

down at one blow Where will the jag - uar go?

Where will the jag - uar go?

Bridge

When the cir - cle is bro - ken When the

crys - tal is cracked When the thread of cre - a-tion is torn We

slip through the veil in - to ter - rors un - known

Where will the jag - uar go?

Coda

Where will the jag - uar go?

In the emerald cathedral
In the valley of clouds
In the span of the branches
Two eyes keep the watch
Where the hummingbird dances
And the snake hesitates
With the calm of command
The jaguar waits
The chainsaw is whining the bulldozer roars
Monkeys are screeching in flight
The spires of the Arawak cut down at one blow
Where will the jaguar go?
Where will the jaguar go?

Under the hammer of hunger
On the anvil of fear
The poor of Sao Paolo
Stream to the frontier
With the promise of farmland
Honest work honest pay
Till the rains unrelenting
Sweep the topsoil away
The captains of cattle take the land cheap
New York and Osaka crave beef
Hooves crush the dirt into dust below
Where will the jaguar go?
Where will the jaguar go?

Bridge:
When the circle is broken
When the crystal is cracked
When the thread of creation is torn
We slip through the veil into terrors unknown
Where will the jaguar go?

In the canyons of commerce
In convoys of light
The armies of loneliness
Drive into the night
Trading plastic for plastic
Making fashion of trash
We are dreaming of love
As love turns to ash
The fires of Prometheus flare to the sky
The seas of the prophets boil dry
This gutted globe was a garden I'm told
Where will the jaguar go?
Where will the jaguar go?
Where will the jaguar go?

Fred singing on the Clearwater Sloop in 1975

Fred performs with Pete Seeger in 1981

SIMPLE LIVING

Of course changing one's own life won't change the world. But if we don't change our own lives, how can we change the world?

♩ = 144

Dropped D Tuning

D

Too man-y words___   too man-y sounds___

Bm

Too man-y at-trac - tions

G

turn me a-round___   Too man-y miles___

in a chrome co-coon___   I nev-er

Em7   A

get an-y-where___   I can't see the moon

Chorus

D

Sim-ple   liv-ing   got to get to

Bm

Sim-ple   liv-ing

Too many words too many sounds
Too many attractions turn me around
Too many miles in a chrome cocoon
I never get anywhere I can't see the moon

Too many commercials too many lies
Too many celebrities I don't recognize
Too many brand names too many magazines
I got so much sensation I can't feel a thing

CHORUS:
Simple . . . living . . .
Simple . . . living . . .
Simple . . . living . . .
Simple . . . living . . .

Too many things we just throw away
If we put it in the garbage we're gonna eat it someday
We turn on the lights and a river dies
We turn the TV on to see an eagle fly

BRIDGE:
Too much work with nothing to do
Too many dreams never come true
Too much hurting without a second glance
Too much desperation they call romance

Gonna take this life pare it to the bone
Baby when you knock baby I'll be home
I'll make my breakfast sweep the floor
Open the windows unlock the door

Gonna turn off the video the audio too
Open my eyes take in the view
See the divine in the veins of a leaf
In the hands of a beggar in the eyes of a thief

CHORUS

Fred performing at the Philadelphia Folk Festival in 1984

Photo: Kate Hastings

WARLORDS

If Tibet or Bosnia sat over trillions of dollars in oil reserves, like the Middle East, would the United States have sat on the sidelines while people were criminally slaughtered? The people of the United States want to do the right thing, but our government cynically drapes greed in high-flown rhetoric.

Copyright 1990 Pine Barrens Music (BMI)

In a dry world in a bar-ren world Wa-ter peo-ple need
wa-ter In the de-sert night a-round the dy-ing light Fit-ful
sleep-ers dream of wa-ter And peace-ful tribes— rule their lives— By
wa-ter And seeth-ing hordes— raise their swords
And kill for wa-ter In a world of drought—
Wa-ter is Lord of all

In a dry world in a barren world
Water people need water
In the desert night around the dying light
Fitful sleepers dream of water
And peaceful tribes rule their lives
By water
And seething hordes raise their swords
And kill for water
In a world of drought
Water is lord of all

In a driven world in a plastic world
Oil we drill for oil
All the meek and the mean choose their dream machines
Line up for oil we shoot up oil
And nation states stake their fate
On the price of oil
And their obedient sons prime their guns
And kill for oil
In a run-down world
Oil is lord of all

BRIDGE:
Oh there's gotta be more than this
The drudging dance the obscene kiss
Oh there's gotta be some way out
A smile a shout

In a hurting world in a hating world
Love we reach for love
In the restless heat of sweat-stained sheets
We strain for love cry out for love
In a child's look an open book
And every page is love
And pushed to shove we kill for love

We cannot kill for love
We cannot kill for love
We cannot kill love

In a desert world
In a driven world
In a doubting world
Love is lord of all
Love is lord of all

Fred with Judy Small (no relation) Faith Petric at the Philadelphia Folk Festival in 1984

Photo: Kate Hastings

GRAVITY

Happiness is no more complicated than remembering to notice the beauty of the world and the persistent goodness of people.

So you see your-self stalk-ing the cit-y

Star-ing straight down— at your feet— You

no-tice the scuff—— on your shoe-shine You a-

void all the holes— in the street— And you

pit-y the drunk in the door-way— While you wave—

— the pan-han-dler a-way— And you

take it as a sign——— of in-sin-cer-i-ty When

some - one says "Have a nice day!"

Chorus

But when Grav - i - ty's drag - gin' you down___ When

grav - i - ty's drag - gin' you down___ When

grav - i - ty's drag - gin' you down___ Look up___

Look up___

Bridge

Look up where the sun___ hits the sky___

line Where the thun - der - heads warn___ of a squall___

___ You don't need___ to be - lieve___ in a mir-

— a- cle   It's a mir-a- cle   to be here at

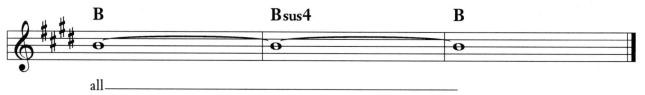

all

CHORUS:
When gravity's draggin' you down
When gravity's draggin' you down
When gravity's draggin' you down
Look up

So you see yourself stalking the city
Staring straight down at your feet
You notice the scuff on your shoeshine
You avoid all the holes in the street
And you pity the drunk in the doorway
While you wave the panhandler away
And you take it as a sign of insincerity
When someone says "Have a nice day!"

But—

CHORUS

Look up where the sun hits the skyline
Where the thunderheads warn of a squall
You don't need to believe in a miracle
It's a miracle to be here at all

Where the bus driver grins through his mustache
And an old woman's lost in her book
And a man is possessed of a paisley vest
That insists upon a second look
And a little girl in a baseball uniform
Is leading her father who's blind
And a man who is muttering under his breath
Is having a very hard time

And—

CHORUS

I have looked in the eyes of the damned and despised
Seen souls no different from mine
And what I perceive in this world I believe
Is no more than I'm looking to find

So—

CHORUS

Fred performs with Greg Artzner of Magpie at the 1984 Philadelphia Folk Festival.

THE LAST TIME I HAD AUTUMN

After the loss of love, every breath, every movement is painful for a while, until the healing comes.

now is bound to make— me—— blue The

last time I had au - tumn I had you The

last time I had au - tumn I had you

you

Bridge

How man - y times— must I pull the car— to the— shoul - der

Just to cry by the side of the road?

How man - y times— must I reach and grasp— at noth - ing

Be - fore I can let you go?

Northfield Minnesota frost upon the plow
The barley and the soybeans are at the feedlot now
Leaves as dry as paper crumble 'neath my tread
Colors of October like memories of the dead

CHORUS:
The last time I saw autumn's fire was a thousand years ago
I put my faith in autumn seasons come seasons go
And every sight of autumn now is bound to make me blue
The last time I had autumn I had you

The crooked streets of Cambridge are skirted now with snow
There's a bookstore crammed with browsers every twenty
  yards or so
And one night last December I searched each one high and
  low
To find the gift you wanted that only I would know

CHORUS:
The last time I felt winter's blast . . .
And every gust of winter now . . .

The last time I had winter I had you
BRIDGE:
How many times must I pull the car to the shoulder
Just to cry by the side of the road?
How many times must I reach and grasp at nothing
Before I can let you go?

In the hills above Las Cruces forget-me-nots have bloomed
I walk the ridge till sundown and whistle a lover's tune
They've put me in the same old bed and the people here are
  kind
I get the urge to call you and put it from my mind

CHORUS:
The last time I breathed springtime air . . .
And every breath of spring now . . .

The last time I had springtime I had you

He who binds to himself a joy

Does the winged life destroy;

But he who kisses the joy as it flies

Lives in eternity's sunrise.

William Blake

Fred talks with students at Oberlin College, 1986

I DIDN'T KNOW

The technology of modern warfare increasingly distances soldiers from the humanity of their victims. I imagined a member of a bombing crew somehow encountering his victim face to face—in a dream or after death or simply after the war, it wasn't clear—and his terrible realization of what he had done.

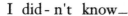

I did-n't know___ you were some-one that I knew___

I did-n't know___ it was you___

I didn't know— they showed me photographs
I didn't know—circles and crosshatches
I didn't know that you had two eyes
I didn't know I would recognize your voice
I had no choice

I didn't know—you can't see much from so high
I didn't know—only the earth and sky
I didn't know about your dignity
I didn't know as the bombs fell silently
Did you even see them?

I didn't know we hit our target clean
I didn't know I'd have these waking dreams
I didn't know under the blanket of flame
I didn't know that you wore my name next to your heart
I was too smart

I didn't know you were someone that I knew
I didn't know it was you

I didn't know—I read the newspapers
I didn't know your hair smelled just like hers
I didn't know you had fingers on each hand
I didn't know you would understand my fear
I see you clearly

I didn't know one day we'd meet like this
I didn't know there could be such peacefulness
I didn't know I could touch your face
I didn't know you would take me in this embrace
It was not wasted

I didn't know you were someone that I knew
I didn't know it was you

There is no greater illusion than fear,

no greater wrong than preparing to defend oneself,

no greater misfortune than having an enemy.

Lao-tzu, *Tao te Ching*

(Stephen Mitchell translation)

LIGHT IN THE HALL

The Massachusetts Chapter of the National Child Rights Alliance asked me to write an anthem they could sing at their gatherings — a "We Shall Overcome" for survivors of child abuse. After hearing Jayne Habe tell her story, I knew an anthem would have to wait. Her story was too powerful, too vivid, too important — it needed to be told.

This song is based on Jayne's recollections and writings.

I'm not singing "Light in the Hall" at my concerts these days. For some of those unprepared for it, the pain of listening to it can be unbearable. But I know from my mail and from countless personal reports that survivors are using the recording in therapy sessions, workshops, and their own living rooms to assist their healing, and I am gratified.

Words by Fred Small and Jayne Habe
Music by Fred Small
Copyright 1989 Pine Barrens Music (BMI)

— end I am fly - ing — a - way — I am dy - ing

Chorus

Is there a cra - dle big e - nough for this lit - tle girl?

It would-n't have to be — so ver - y big

For a girl and a

ted - dy bear and a patch - work quilt —

It's wait - ing some - where for me

There's a light in the hall
There's a crack in the doorway lets it into my room
Tells me everything tells me everything
I curl up in a ball
Try to slide in the crack between the bed and the wall
I am falling I am falling

Daddy they'll know
I'll walk funny and they'll know I've been bad
Daddy please don't please don't please don't
I'm shaking all over
I squeeze my legs together just as tight as I can
You can't you can't you can okay okay okay

BRIDGE:
I see the tree through the window
The tree is my friend
I see the moon through the clouds
And the stars without end
I am flying away I am dying

CHORUS:
Is there a cradle big enough for this little girl
It wouldn't have to be so very big
For a girl and a teddy bear and a patchwork quilt
It's waiting somewhere for me

Don't you tell anyone

If you know what's good for you
And your little sister don't you love your sister
And who would believe you
Just a little girl with a big imagination
Everyone knows me I'm an important man

I get ready for school
My hair is brushed and pulled tight in a bow
But I am dirty I am dirty
Mommy puts on my coat
Red and purple blotches up and down my legs
She won't look at me she won't look at me

BRIDGE:
I will run to the park
I will climb on the swing
I will swing so high
Up above everything
Till a cloud takes me away

CHORUS

Now I am grown
On a silver chain I wear a pretty stone

A friend gave me to say she loves me
And to say I can love
And to say I am worthy of it
It is not easy it is not easy

Sometimes I scream
Sometimes I weep like the little girl
I never was I never was
I tell the story
Somebody stole my life but I'm taking it back
I can see colors I can see colors now

BRIDGE:
Tracing the truth through the tangle of lies
Forgiving myself what I did to survive
I am living I am living

CHORUS

THE DISTANCE

No song of mine has been more painful to write, because I lived it. Most of my songs are about healing. This one is about how bad it feels. But acknowledging how bad it feels is where healing begins.

♩ = 120

C
We pass through these rooms with-out speak-ing Where the

F
light throws a pat-tern of lace— You say you don't know if you are

C   **Dm**
leav-ing But there's no— shad-ow— of doubt up-on your—

G   **F**   **C**
— face And you tell— me there is no— oth-er— And I

F   **C**   **G**
know you well e-nough— to know it's— true— And

Am   **F**
well e-nough— to know you need a lov-er Who can

give   what   I   nev-er   gave   to   you   And   you   can

Chorus

say   that   you   were   lone-ly   when   I   lay   right   by   your   side

You   can   say   you   saw   the   dis-tance   When   I

looked   you   in   the   eye   And   you   can   say   I   nev-er

reached   you   no   mat-ter   how   man-y   times   I   tried   But   don't

say   I   did-n't   love   you   'Cause   that's   a   god   damn   lie

Bridge

And   it   seems   some-times   like   I   lost   my   hand   to   a   ma-chine   In   an

ac-ci-dent   a   long   time   a-go   It   grabbed   at   my   fin-gers   and

tore them off clean Still I— wait for these fin-gers— to

grow And if I— had fin-gers I'd touch your cheek with a

ges-ture so— gen-tle and fine I would braid your hair with

ba - by's— breath I would take your hand in mine

Coda

I know you won't say I— did-n't love you 'Cause you

know it would— be a lie—

We pass through these rooms without speaking
Where the light throws a pattern of lace
You say you don't know if you are leaving
But there's no shadow of doubt upon your face
And you tell me there is no other
And I know you well enough to know it's true
And well enough to know you need a lover
Who can give what I never gave to you 'Cause

CHORUS:
You can say that you were lonely
When I lay right by your side
You can say you saw the distance
When I looked you in the eye
And you can say I never reached you
No matter how many times I tried
But don't say I didn't love you
'Cause that's a god damn lie

I emptied the drawer filled with letters
And I bowed my head and cried
No one ever loved me better
There was love in every line
But there were times I didn't hold you
When all you needed was a touch
And there were times when I said nothing
When one word would have been enough

Bridge:
And it seems sometimes like I lost my hand to a machine
In an accident a long time ago
It grabbed at my fingers and tore them off clean
Still I wait for these fingers to grow
And if I had fingers I'd touch your cheek
With a gesture so gentle and fine
I would braid your hair with baby's breath
I would take your hand in mine And

CHORUS

I hear your voice in the morning
Singing softly to yourself
I know you imagine the loving
That awaits you with somebody else
And maybe I will find another
Who will take me in spite of these scars
And each of us yet may discover
How innocent we are 'Cause

CHORUS

Your pain is the breaking of the shell
that encloses your understanding.

Kahil Gibran

MISTAKEN IDENTITY

The ability to distinguish the present from the past is the mark of healing.

♩ = *144*

C   G

I touch your hand   It's not my hand you feel

C   Em

It's the hand of an-oth-er man   It's the touch of a

A

dan-ger-ous time   It's the blow that leaves— no trace—

C   D

It's the face of the per-fect crime—

Chorus

C   D   Em

Mis-tak-en i-den-ti-ty   I am not the man—

C

Look at my— face   I am not the man—

Em   C   G

Bridge

Sun-light— fil-ters through the leaves   A breeze blows

the cur-tain wide   Chil-dren play a-cross— the street

And I am by— your side—   But I get— con-fused

And I am— fright-ened— too   Am I the beast—

— in the shad-ow   Or am I here with you?

Coda

Please take this   boy   for who I am—

Can we lay down this fear and love each oth-er?

fear and love each oth-er   — fear

I touch your hand
It's not my hand you feel
It's the hand of another man
It's the touch of a dangerous time
It's the blow that leaves no trace
It's the face of the perfect crime

CHORUS:
Mistaken identity
I am not the man
Look at my face
I am not the man

I whisper your name
It's not my voice you hear
It's the voice of the waking dead
It's the father of original sin
It's the brother of unlocked doors
It's the lover of broken skin

CHORUS

BRIDGE:
Sunlight filters through the leaves
A breeze blows the curtains wide
Children play across the street
And I am by your side

But I get confused
And I am frightened too
Am I the beast in the shadow
Or am I here with you?

CHORUS:
Mistaken identity
I am not the man
Look at my face
Please take this boy for who I am

Can we lay down this fear and love each other?
Can we lay down this fear and love each other?
Can we lay down this fear?

Fred performs in Japan in 1988

ALL THE TIME IN THE WORLD

We're always too busy, it seems. But too busy with what? If we devote ourselves to the things that are really important, and let go of those that aren't, we actually have all the time in the world.

All the time in the world
for the prom-is-es worth keep-ing
And the prom-is-es some-times
we must break

I have no time for heedless hurry
I have no time for the hustler's bluff
I have no time for restless worry
I have all the time in the world for love

I have no time to chase perfection
I have no time for the rock of righteousness
I have no time for cruel correction
I have all the time in the world for tenderness

All the time in the world to watch you when you're sleeping
All the time in the world to kiss you when you wake
All the time in the world for the promises worth keeping
And the promises sometimes we must break

I have no time for the veils of violence
I have no time for walls without release
I have no time for the smiles of tyrants
I have all the time in the world for peace

All the time in the world to watch you when you're sleeping
All the time in the world to kiss you when you wake
All the time in the world for the promises worth keeping
And the promises sometimes we must break

I have no time for pretty poison
I have no time for what is not true
I have no time for quiet desperation
I have all the time in the world for you
I have all the time in the world for you

Modern man thinks he loses something—time—when he does not do things quickly; yet
he does not know what to do with the time he gains—except kill it.

Erich Fromm

GUINEVERE AND THE FIRE

Rhonda Parkyns told me this true story of her mother's childhood when I was on tour in Australia in April of 1992. (The final scene between Gwen and the Aboriginal woman is fiction, but tells the truth.)

Chorus

Lit - tle white girls have dis - ap - peared_____ They

drink and dance when the moon is red Bet - ter

nev - er let 'em see your gol - den hair

Bridge

Now she runs___ till her feet are bleed - ing

To the house up - on___ the hill___ Now

comes the doc - tor's wag - on speed - ing

To her moth - er___ cold and still_____

Based on a true story.

My grandmother was born in 1900
On a farm in New South Wales
She wed a dairyman
Who liked to raise a pint of ale
The first child came when she was 20
Five more babes in seven years
That first daughter was my mother
They called her Guinevere

Little Gwen would play beneath the willow
"Yes the Queen would love some tea"
Helped with chores that never ended
Tried to mind tried to please
Sometimes she heard the music
Wild and strange in the summer night
"They're dirty people" warned her mother
"Never go near their campfire light"

CHORUS:
Stay away from the camp of the blackfellas
Little white girls have disappeared
They drink and dance when the moon is red
Better never let 'em see your golden hair

Came the winter of '27
So cold the milk froze in the pail
Her mum hung the nappies by the hearth
Her dad in town for a round of ale
A spark leapt from the fire that night
Wrapped her mother in a gown of flame
Flailing dancing in a frenzy
Falling down in voiceless pain

Stillness and the stench of burning
Then so soft 'twas like a ghost
"Fetch the Cunninghams" she whispered
"Bring me aid or I am lost"
The Cunningham house was not two miles away
And they the nearest whites
Past the camp of the Aboriginals
Past the demons of the night

CHORUS

"I will run to save my mother
I must go now I must fly"
Still she heard her mother's tales
Of the Devil's drums and the evil eye
Her mother's breathing ever fainter
Gwen frozen in her fright
Seven hours till dawn she waited
For the safety of the light

Bridge:
Now she runs till her feet are bleeding
To the house upon the hill
Now comes the doctor's wagon speeding
To her mother cold and still

They laid her down in the Nowra graveyard
From the Bible read a verse
Children sent to aunts and uncles
Some to Melbourne some to Perth
Gwen packed her canvas satchel
Could not hold the salt tears back
Turned to leave her home forever
Faced a woman gnarled and black

"Child our hearts are heavy
Grieving for your loss
We live so close by you
Why did you not come to us?
We have salves to heal the burning
We have herbs to stop the pain
We could have helped had we but known
To make your mother whole again"

CHORUS (twice)

Fred autographs an album for a Japanese fan

THE OTHER SIDE OF THE WOOD

When someone is hurting, my impulse is to snuggle in close. Sometimes that's exactly what they need. But other times they need to work things out alone, and the greatest gift one can give is solitude.

We met in the qui-et of— the mead-ow—

We ram-bled hand in hand— through— the glade—

We lay en-twined— on— a pal-let—

Of clo-ver— and col-um-bine made—

But now the for-est fills— with shad-ows

And the ra-ven and the wolf— call— your name—

And you won-der how you ev-er came— to wan-der

— Is it poss-i-ble— I am— your friend?—

Coda

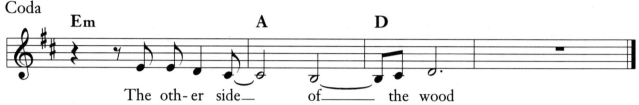

The oth-er side— of— the wood

We met in the quiet of the meadow
We rambled hand in hand through the glade
We lay entwined on a pallet
Of clover and columbine made
But now the forest fills with shadows
And the raven and the wolf call your name
And you wonder how you ever came to wander
So deep into this unknown terrain

CHORUS:
So go your way I cannot hold you
Nor would I detain you if I could
I will wait for you in the clearing
On the other side of the wood

How I would speed to your rescue
Through the darkwood so wild and overgrown
But where you go I cannot follow
The staff you hew must be your own
For my comfort would only confine you
And my love would close about you like a shroud
All my fears for you would confound you
All my fears for myself would drag you down

CHORUS

Bridge:
I know the wind will tell you stories
And every tale come to a bloody end
But somewhere in that dread parade of possibilities
Is it possible I am your friend

To walk with a companion is a blessing
To forfeit one's freedom is a curse
To open the heart's wounds is agony
To bind them tight is even worse
Wherever the light before you leads you
And whether you find me or no
My love will travel softly at your shoulder
And abide with you wherever you may go

CHORUS

Intimate relationships are not safe! That is not their nature.
They unmask and expose us, and bring us face to face with life in all its power and
mystery, through contact with what is most different from us–an other.

John Welwood

Fred staffing a table for the Cambridge Environmental Citizen Organization, Earth Day 1991

HOT FROGS ON THE LOOSE

Don't worry, the nuclear industry says. It's perfectly safe, they promise. We've thought of every contingency, they tell us. **Ribbit!**

♩ = 170

Em

By the light of the Ten - nes - see moon From the

C

bil - ious bub - bles of a black la - goon— They make a

D   **C** **D** **Em** *Repeat figure*

hound dog howl a SWAT team swoon Hot frogs on the loose—

Chorus **G**   **D**

Hip - pi - ty hop - pi - ty here they come Ra - di - o - ac - tive

Em   **D**   **C**   **A**

look-in' for fun If you kiss— 'em look out— for the tongue—

C   **D**   **Em**

Hot frogs on the loose— Glub Glub

C   **C**

Ahhh! Glub Glub Ahhh! Glub Glub

By the light of the Tennessee moon
From the bilious bubbles of a black lagoon
They make a hound dog howl a SWAT team swoon
Hot frogs on the loose

They've multiplied since '53
Slurping nuclear debris
Amphibious fabulous fancy free
Hot frogs on the loose

CHORUS:
Hippity hoppity here they come
Radioactive lookin' for fun
If you kiss 'em look out for the tongue
Hot frogs on the loose

They got little skinny legs and big bug eyes
Fraternizing's not advised
They like you like they like flies
Hot frogs on the loose

They got a chicken nugget body and a whopper leap
In your bedroom while you sleep
They'll make your Geiger counter beep
Hot frogs on the loose

CHORUS

BRIDGE:
You can put the pedal to the metal till the rubber squeals
Squish 'em with your tires you got hot wheels
Now you know how it feels to be a
Hot frog on the loose

Please do not keep them as pets
Sautéing them may bring regrets
Make a citizen's arrest of a
Hot frog on the loose

Frogs for peace frogs for defense
Don't be nervous don't be tense
We've got a sure-fire three-foot fence
To keep the hot frogs from gettin' loose

CHORUS

SMILE WHEN YOU'RE READY

A smile is a wonderful gift to ourselves and to the world. How many times has your day suddenly gone better because someone smiled at you? But a smile must spring forth in its own time, not be pasted on under duress or because others find our sadness inconvenient.

♩ = 158

Lit- tle girl— in Mar - y Janes   You walked— a fine line   Par- ty braids— and— pin-a-fores—

"Thank you for the ver- y nice time"   They did-n't ask— what you were think-ing   They did-n't want to know   All you want-ed was—

— to be loved   So you put— on a show——   But you can

Chorus   smile——— when you're read-y   Not a mo-ment be-fore—

Little girl in Mary Janes
You walked a fine line
Party braids and pinafores
"Thank you for the very nice time"
They didn't ask what you were thinking
They didn't want to know
All you wanted was to be loved
So you put on a show

CHORUS:
But you can smile when you're ready
Not a moment before
A refugee awakes at night
To the sound of distant wars
Smile when you're ready
No matter how long it takes
Your wounded heart will find
Its own saving grace

Toy guns and bloody noses
"Don't walk away from a fight"
"Faggot" jeers at the sign of tears
Screw the lid on tight
So you never let 'em see you
You never laugh too loud
You're the man in the iron mask
You're a big boy now

CHORUS

Rain on the river
Patches of blue
Just when a smile seems a million miles away
It'll sneak up on you

Sometimes the people who hurt you
Don't leave you alone
Maybe they ask forgiveness
Maybe they say please come home
Maybe they're just too ashamed to admit
The things you say are true
You can love 'em you can let 'em go
You know it's up to you

CHORUS (to . . .)

Fred with an Australian fan in 1992

RODNEY KING'S BLESSING

Two days into the bloody Los Angeles riots of 1992, Rodney King — the man beaten by the police officers whose subsequent acquittal sparked the riots — went before the television cameras and, with halting eloquence, appealed for peace. All the words in the song are his.

Words from the statement by Rodney King, Los Angeles, May 1, 1992
Music by Fred Small copyright 1992 Pine Barrens Music (BMI)

CHORUS:
People can we all get along?
Can we can we all get along?
People you know we're all stuck here for a while
Let's try to work it out

People I just want to say you know
Can we get along
Can we all get along
Can we stop making it
Making it hard
For the older people and the kids

Bridge:
I mean we've got enough smog
Here in Los Angeles
Let alone to get killed
Setting these fires and things
It's just not right
It's not right
It's not going to change anything
We'll get our justice

CHORUS

They've won the battle
But they haven't won the war
We'll have our day in court
That's all we want
I love I'm neutral
I love people of every color
I'm not like they're making me out to be

Bridge:
We've got to quit
I mean I could understand
The first two hours after the verdict
But to go on like this
To see that security guard
Shot on the ground—it's just not right
Because those people will never
Go home to their families again

CHORUS (We can . . .)

Fred with Judy Small (no relation) at the 1992 National Folk Festival of Australia

FRIENDS FIRST

I once saw a Nicole Hollander "Sylvia" poster that showed a uniformed police officer, captioned "The Love Cop," with the saying "Lust makes you stupid." This song is about reconciling love and intelligence, or trying to!

Capo on 2nd Fret

♩ = 100

I wake up ear - ly— in the cool of the morn - ing Ma-gen - ta and pur-ple o - ver Cas - co— Bay— Sleep-less with yearn - ing rea - son re - turn - ing I send you this song— like a sum - mer bou - quet— I want to be

Chorus

Friends first— be - fore we are lov - ers Friends first— tak - ing our own sweet time— Friends first— lay your head on my shoul - der

Tell me your sto - ry and I'll tell you____ mine____

Bridge

Two ag - ed lov - ers sit by the fire____ A

look car - ries mean - ing on - ly old friends could know A

life - time____ to - geth - er come down to em - bers And their

fac - es are filled_ with the light from be - low_____

I wake up early in the cool of the morning
Magenta and purple over Casco Bay
Sleepless with yearning reason returning
I send you this song like a summer bouquet

I want to be

CHORUS:
Friends first before we are lovers
Friends first taking our own sweet time
Friends first lay your head on my shoulder
Tell me your story and I'll tell you mine

We've both tasted the passion of reckless abandon
Drinking our pleasure like blackberry wine
And wakened in panic in the arms of a stranger
Darling let's do it different this time

CHORUS

BRIDGE:
Two aged lovers sit by the fire
A look carries meaning only old friends can know
A lifetime together come down to embers
And their faces are filled with the light from below

Tell me your bad dreams sing me your lullabies
When did you run away and when did you fight
Show me the caterpillar show me the butterfly
We'll get as close as the wind and the night

CHORUS

TOO MANY PEOPLE

Most of us have a pretty good idea of the disastrous impact of population growth on the environment but prefer not to talk about it because it raises difficult, controversial, and sometimes personal issues. What does one say to friends expecting their third child? It's a little late for a ZPG lecture! So here, in lieu of lecture, is a song—a sing-along, no less—much more fun than a lecture!

CHORUS:
Too many people having too many babies
Got to love them babies but there's
Too many people having too many babies
Got to love them babies but it's out of control

Adam and Eve time on their hands
Hyperactive glands room to expand
Once they began begatting they begatted to excess
Eschewing tactics prophylactic now we're in a mess
Because there's

CHORUS

When Columbus sailed the ocean we were 400 million
Industrial revolution still under a billion
The Great Depression hit 2.1 billion
Now we're pushing the millennium 6 billion and counting

BRIDGE:
Civil wars rumbling refugees stumbling
Forests falling deserts creeping
Traffic crawling resources depleting
Shoppers shopping for pleasures fleeting

When there's

CHORUS

Once I lived in the city it was too big and noisy
So I moved to the country to stop and smell the rosies
All my city friends joined me and put up nice new housies
Now it's too big and noisy think I'll move to the country

BRIDGE:
Some say no no no no it's not the population
It's consumption pollution unequal distribution
I say that's so but it's a simple equation
Population times pollution equals no solution

When there's

CHORUS

If you are a child welcome to the world
This blue-green earth is your gift by birth
May you rock to its rhythms may you sing its anthems
And if you have babies please stop at two

Because there's

CHORUS

CHORUS (. . . please stop at two)

Fred at the 1991 Kerrville Folk Festival

IF I WERE TAKEN NOW

Life is so fragile, love so precious. Let's live each moment as if it were our last—and our first.

pi-lot me in-to the night   I would not be fright-ened_

But I would miss you   I would miss you

If I were taken now
I would remember the light in your hair
The darkness at the center of your eye
If I were taken now
I would remember the small of your back
The arc of your shoulder

If I were taken now
I would give thanks
For the kindness you showed
In loving me so easily

If I were taken now
I would remember your breath on my cheek
The soft conspiracy of your kiss
If I were taken now
I would remember how quickly you laugh
Warm as winter's kitchen

If I were taken now
I would ask forgiveness
For every time my thoughtlessness caused you pain
Or made you doubt me

A swarm of stars
A fleet of fireflies
Would pilot me into the night
I would not be frightened
But I would miss you
I would miss you

Every moment is an opportunity, which will never come again, to love.

John Bell

THE MARINE'S LAMENT OR THE PINK PERIL

The ferociously homophobic reaction to President Clinton's attempt to lift the ban on gays and lesbians in the military should not have surprised us, I suppose. But so much hatred ain't a pretty sight. Like all hatred, it springs from fear—fear of the unknown, the different, and of the feminine within every man.

Some of my friends object that this song isn't affirming, understanding or inclusive. Well, true! But compared to how angry I was after listening to the viciousness vented on talk radio, the song is very, very mild.

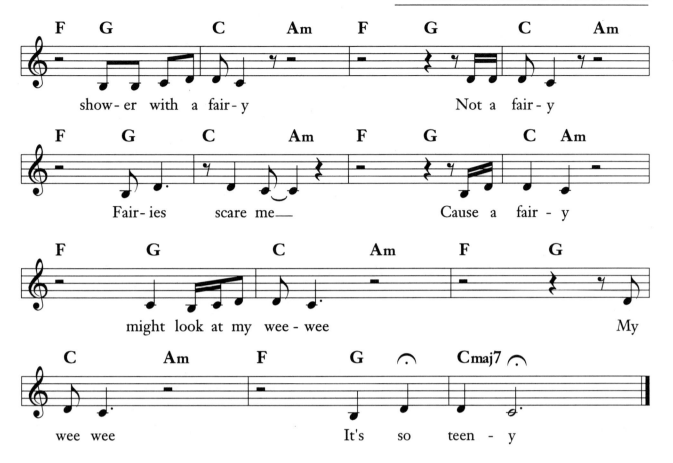

From the halls of Montezuma
To the shores of Tripoli
I have fought my country's battles
I have faced every enemy

I ain't scared of no Iraqi missiles
I ain't scared of no Russian tanks
If I'm captured and tortured all they'll get
Is my serial number name and rank

You know I'd storm Baghdad to kick Saddam's butt
Swim to Havana bring home Castro's beard
For my buddies throw my body on a live grenade
I guess I just don't know the meaning of fear

But please
Please
Please please please please please
Don't make me
Shower with a fairy
Not a fairy
Fairies scare me
Cause a fairy
Might look at my weewee
My weewee
It's so teeny

Hatred is the coward's revenge for being intimidated.

George Bernard Shaw

THE HUG SONG

This is the "all ages" version.

Capo on 2nd Fret
♩ = 176

C
When I was a lit - tle bit - ty ba - by child— my

F   **G**   **C**
ma - ma used to hold me tight— My dad - dy used to come and

D7   **G**
pick me up— When I got scared at night— The

C   **Em**   **Dm**
years have passed— I've— grown so fast and most - ly I— feel

C   **G**   **C**
strong But tim - id or bold I'm

F   **G**   **C**   **G**   Chorus
nev - er too old— to sing— this co - zy song I want a

C   **F**
hug when we say hel - lo— I want a hug when it's

time to go— I want a hug 'cause I want you to know— I'm aw-ful-ly fond of you— I want a hug — what a won-der-ful feel - ing 'want a hug — to feel you squeez - ing 'want a hug — it cer-tain-ly seems— like the nat-u-ral thing to do—

When I was a little bitty baby child, my momma used to hold me tight
My daddy used to come and pick me up when I got scared at night
The years have passed I've grown so fast and mostly I feel strong
But timid or bold I'm never too old to sing this cozy song

CHORUS:
I want a hug when we say hello
I want a hug when it's time to go
I want a hug 'cause I want you to know
I'm awfully fond of you.
I want a hug–what a wonderful feeling
Want a hug–to feel you squeezing
Want a hug–it certainly seems like the natural thing to do

CHOURS

Now some folks don't like hugging–they think they're too tough
I bet they'd be a whole lot friendlier if they were just hugged enough
When you hug the ones who love you an amazing thing you learn
When you give a hug you just can't help but get one in return

CHOURS

Sometimes grownups are grouchy and they put the blame on you
Sometimes you make just a little mistake though you did the best you could do
Sometimes love is everywhere and it's a beautiful day
And everytime is the perfect time to open your arms and say

CHOURS

EVERYTHING POSSIBLE

The funny thing about this song, which now may be the best know and best loved, is that when I wrote it I wasn't even sure it was a keeper. Since then the Flirtations, Motherlode, Roy Bailey, Cathy Fink & Marcy Marxer, Priscilla Herdman, Justina & Joyce, countless gay and lesbian choruses have carried it all over the world. But to me the most gratifying performance is whenever a parent sings it to a child.

I will sing you a song— no one— sang to me—

may it keep you good com-pan-y

Chorus

You can— be an-y— bo-dy— you want to

be, you can— love whom-ev-er you will—

You can trav-el an-y— coun-try where your heart leads—

— and know I will— love you still

You can live by your-self— you can gath-er friends a-round—

— you can— choose one— spe-cial— one—

and the on - ly mea-sure of your words and your deeds

will be the love you leave be - hind when you're done

Bridge

Don't be rat-tled by names, by taunts, by

games, but seek out spir - its true

If you give your friends the best part of your-self

they will give the same back to you.

We have cleared off the table, the leftovers saved
Washed the dishes and put them away
I have told you a story and tucked you in tight
At the end of your knockabout day
As the moon sets its sails to carry you to sleep
Over the midnight sea
I will sing you a song no one sang to me.
May it keep you good company.

CHORUS:
You can be anybody you want to be
You can love whomever you will
You can travel any country where your heart leads
And know I will love you still
You can live by yourself, you can gather friends around
You can choose one special one
And the only measure of your words and your deeds
Will be the love you leave behind when you're done.

There are girls who grow up strong and bold
There are boys quiet and kind
Some race on ahead, some follow behind
Some go in their own way and time
Some women love women, some men love men
Some raise children, some never do
You can dream all the day never reaching the end
Of everything possible for you.

Don't be rattled by names, by taunts, by games

But seek out spirits true

If you give your friends the best part of yourself

They will give the same back to you.

CHORUS

PEACE IS

Singing together is to me the heart of folk music–the moment when we stop playing "performer" and "audience" and become a community, and each of us is reminded of the power within in us and around us. "Peace Is" is a song to sing together.

© Pine Barrens Music (BMI)

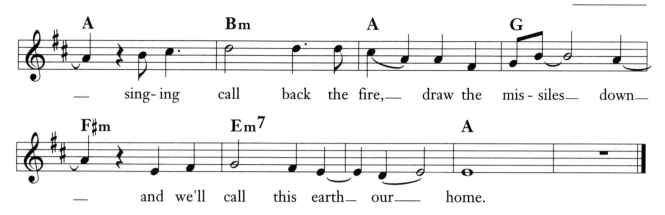

sing-ing   call   back   the   fire,—   draw the   mis - siles—   down—

and we'll   call   this   earth—   our—   home.

Feel the cool breeze blowing through the smoke and the heat
Hear the gentle voices and the marching feet
Singing call back the fire, draw the missiles down
And we'll call this earth our home.

CHORUS:
Peace is the bread we break
Love is the river rolling
Life is a chance we take
When we make this earth our home
Gonna make this earth our home.

We have known the atom, the power and pain
We've seen people fall beneath the killing rain
If the mind still reasons and the soul remains
It shall never be again.

CHORUS

Peace grows from a tiny seed
As the acorn grows into the tallest tree
Many years ago I heard a soldier say
When people want peace, better get out of the way.

CHORUS

NOTES ON THE CHORDS

I know no greater honor as a songwriter than when someone chooses, from all the millions of songs that have been written, to sing one of mine. Thanks to all of you who make that choice. The diagrams below are intended to make it a little easier for you guitar players! If you want to know more about how I play a particular song, please grab me after a concert and I'll be happy to show you.

I play most of my songs in standard concert tuning: E-A-D-G-B-E. I use conventional folk-style chords, favoring these patterns:

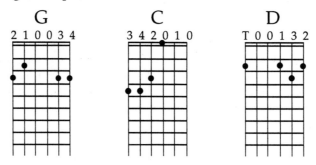

Playing in the key of E, as on "Gravity" and "Too Many People," I'll often use these voicings for A and B (sounding all strings):

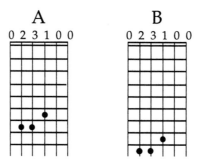

Playing in the key of D, I always tune the sixth (bass) string down a whole step from E to D. This is called Dropped D tuning and gives a strong, rich sound. Here are some common chords in this tuning:

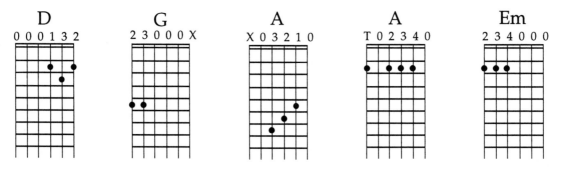

On "The Other Side of the Wood," I use DADGAD tuning. DADGAD is how the strings are tuned, from sixth to first: D-A-D-G-A-D. DADGAD is a lustrous, bittersweet tuning with lots of surprising suspensions. (My thanks to Allen Power for sending me his DADGAD primer.) Here are some of the chords I use in DADGAD:

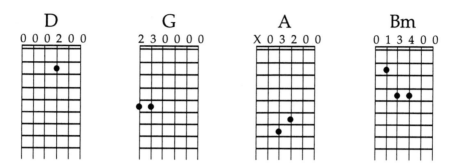

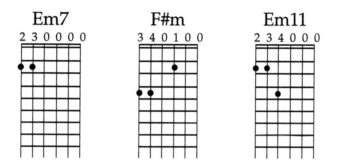

This is an index of song titles and first lines. Song titles are **Bold**.